Student-Made Shape Booklets

Reproducibles For Four Complete Booklets

Spring
(Grades 2–3)

Booklet 1:	**Kites**
Booklet 2:	**Dinosaurs**
Booklet 3:	**Frogs**
Booklet 4:	**Butterflies**

Concept created by
Dawn E. Tullis

Edited and written by
Becky S. Andrews
Diane Badden
Lynn Bemer
Lori Bruce

Illustrated by
Pam Crane
Susan Hodnett
Rebecca Saunders
Barry Slate
Jennifer Tipton

Table Of Contents

Kites Booklet

Dinosaurs Booklet

Table Of Contents
(continued)

Frogs Booklet

Frogs Booklet

Butterflies Booklet

Butterflies Booklet

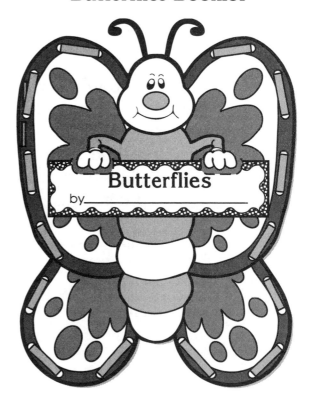

About This Book

• Four separate booklets for your students to make
• Directions provided on each page
• Learning combined with activities your students enjoy

Easy As 1, 2, 3!

1. Choose one of the booklets and reproduce the pages for each student in your class.

2. Allow each child to complete his own booklet independently, or work together as a class in a teacher-directed activity.

3. Have each child proudly take his booklet home to show what he has accomplished.

Suggestions For Management

• Duplicate one page per week for students, or provide a new page daily.

• If desired, adapt the activities to your students' abilities by masking the problems and directions and reprogramming with another skill before duplicating.

• Collect students' completed pages and save them until booklets are ready to be assembled. Demonstrate how to make booklet covers and assemble the pages.

Kites

by

_____

Note To Teacher: Duplicate one copy per student on light blue construction paper. See page 16 for directions to complete the covers.

1

Color.
Cut and paste.

Fly High

Name _____

Kite Kits

Name _____

Complete each kite kit.
Cut out and glue the matching string holder in the box.
Write the word in the blank.

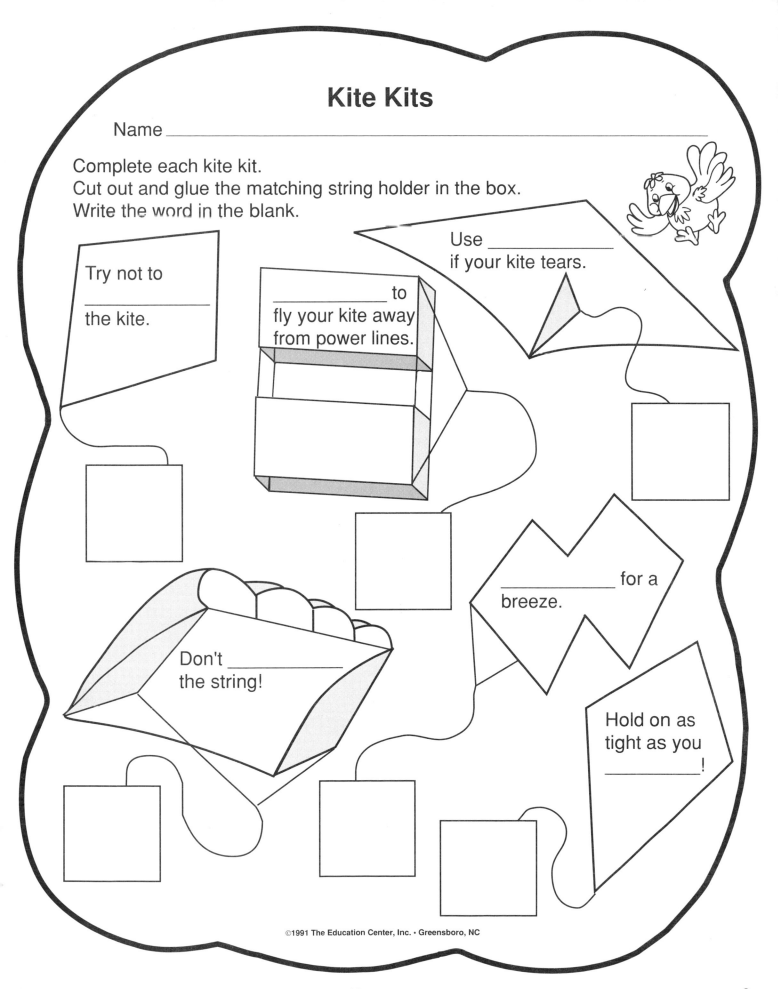

Try not to
_____
the kite.

_____ to
fly your kite away
from power lines.

Use _____
if your kite tears.

_____ for a
breeze.

Don't _____
the string!

Hold on as
tight as you
_____!

Color.
Cut and paste.

Up And Down

Name _____

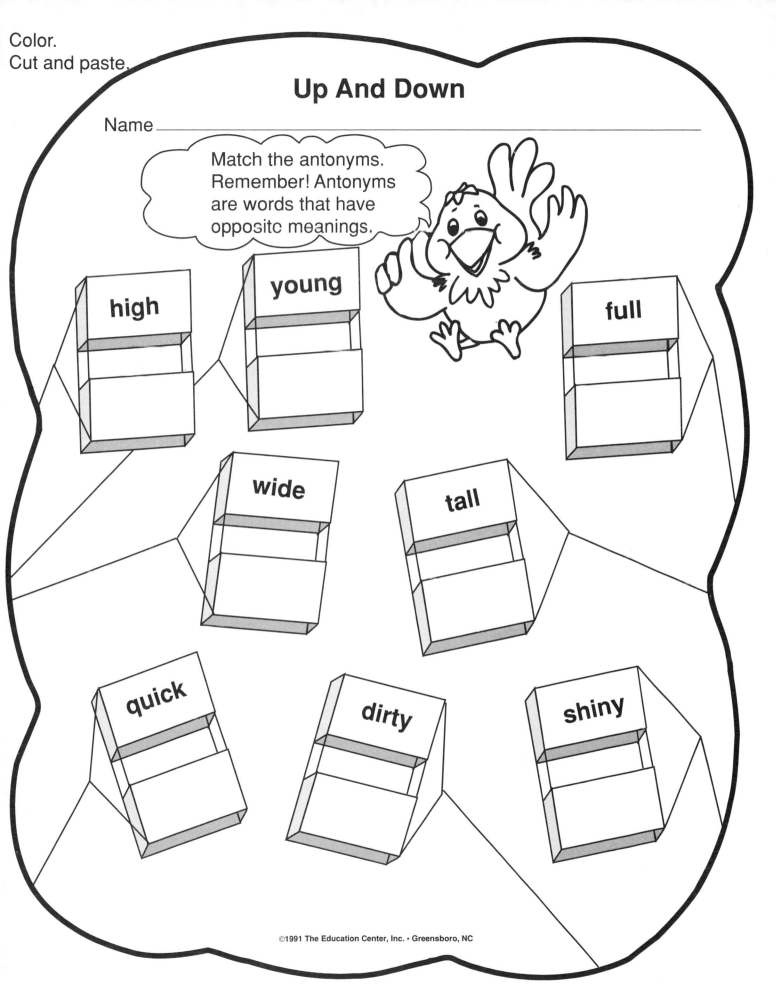

Match the antonyms. Remember! Antonyms are words that have opposite meanings.

high

young

full

wide

tall

quick

dirty

shiny

Fly High Pieces
Use with page 2.

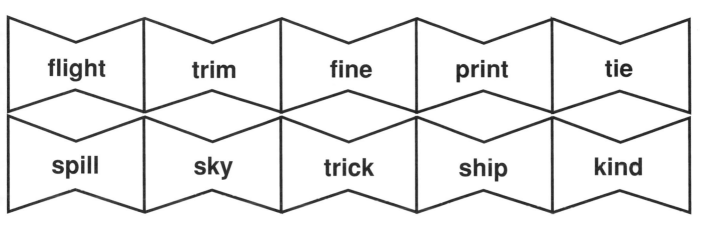

flight | trim | fine | print | tie

spill | sky | trick | ship | kind

Kite Kits Pieces
Use with page 3.

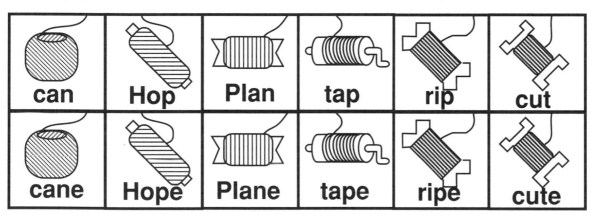

| can | Hop | Plan | tap | rip | cut |
| cane | Hope | Plane | tape | ripe | cute |

Up And Down Pieces
Use with page 4.

slow	short	empty	old
clean	low	narrow	dull

Sky High

Name _____

Solve the problems.
Find each answer in a cloud.
Glue cotton on the cloud to cover the answer.

73 53 60 42

75 92 48 80

84 71 98 28 77

53

| 35 | 28 | 64 | 24 | 49 | 38 |
| + 25 | + 47 | + 28 | + 47 | + 28 | + 35 |

| 34 | 69 | 57 | 37 | 17 | 19 |
| + 19 | + 29 | + 23 | + 47 | + 25 | + 29 |

Write the two numbers you did not cover in the boxes.
Add the numbers.
If their sum is **81**, you are "flying high" with addition!

⬜
⬜
+ ⬜

Note To Teacher: Supply each student with approximately four cotton balls to complete this page. Have each student gently pull his cotton balls into thin wisps before gluing them to his page.

Soaring With Synonyms

Name _____

Match the synonyms.
Use string to connect each
kite to a flier.
Glue the string at each • .

Remember! Synonyms are
words that have about the
same meaning.

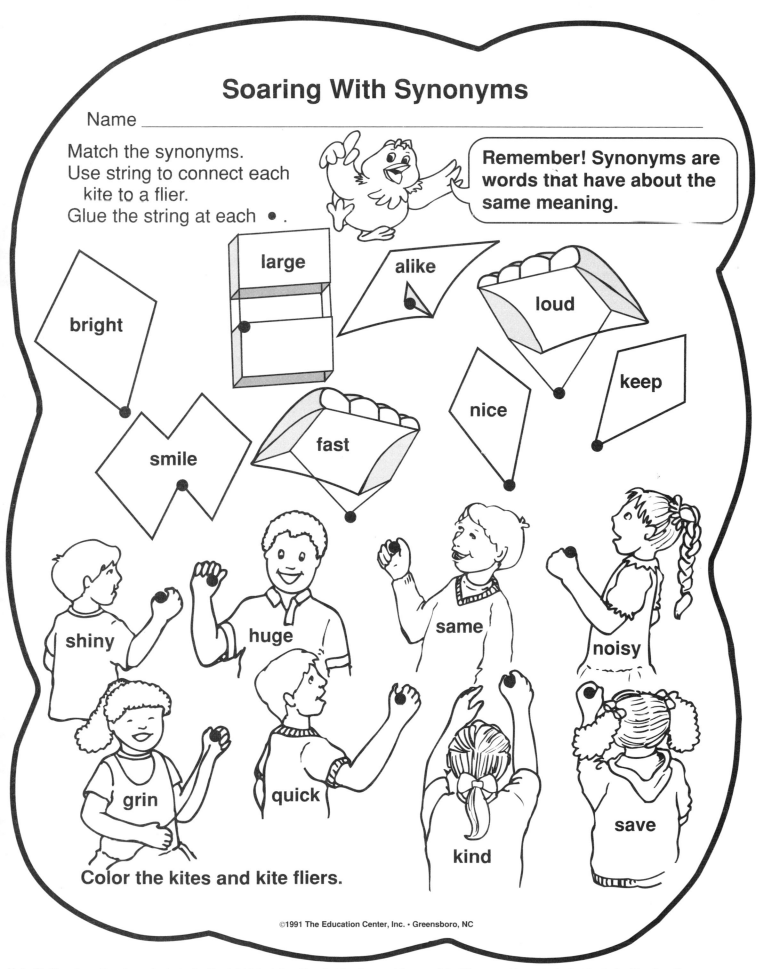

Color the kites and kite fliers.

©1991 The Education Center, Inc. • Greensboro, NC

Note To Teacher: Supply each student with eight 6-inch lengths of string (or yarn) to complete this page. Have students trim their string lengths as needed.

7

Puzzling Fliers

Name _____

The word **fly** has many meanings.
Cut out and glue a matching piece to each bow.
Write the word in the blank.

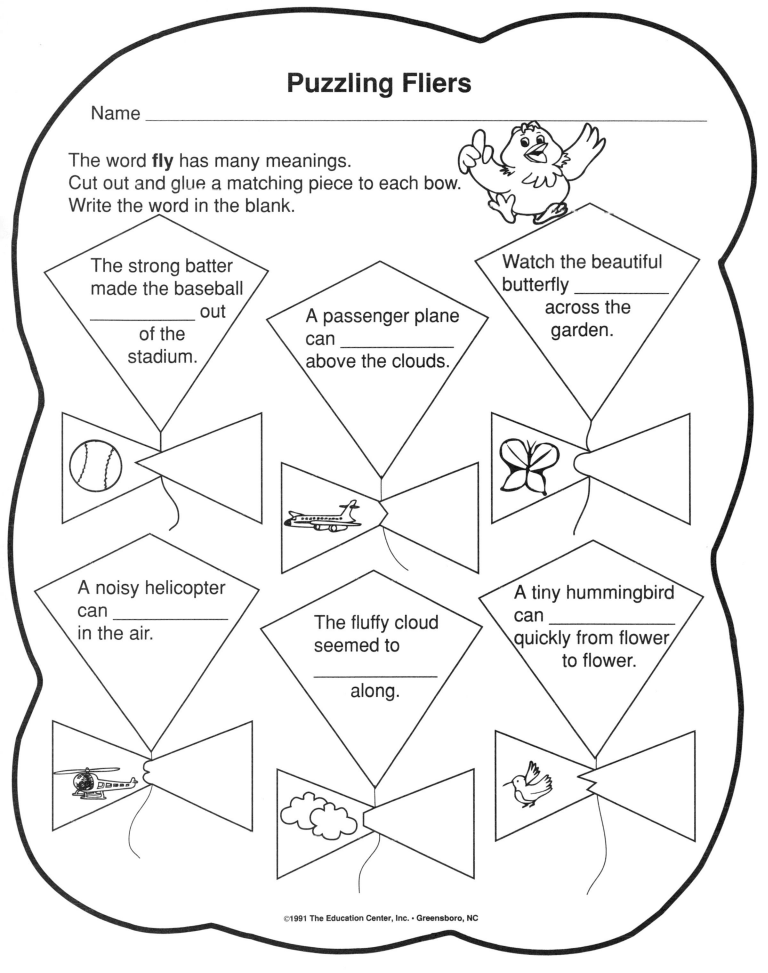

The strong batter made the baseball _____ out of the stadium.

A passenger plane can _____ above the clouds.

Watch the beautiful butterfly _____ across the garden.

A noisy helicopter can _____ in the air.

The fluffy cloud seemed to _____ along.

A tiny hummingbird can _____ quickly from flower to flower.

©1991 The Education Center, Inc. • Greensboro, NC

Note To Teacher: Duplicate "Puzzling Fliers Pieces" on page 16 to complete this page.

8

Kite-flying Fun

Name _____

Help Kevin put the kite-flying steps in order.
Number the boxes from 1 to 5.
Color the pictures.

Then put the kite together.
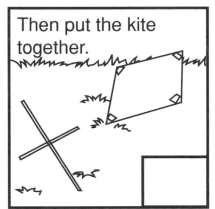

Next have a friend help you launch the kite.

Next tie string to the kite and add a tail.

First find an open field away from power lines.
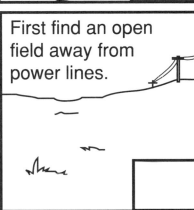

After that tie bows to the tail.

Complete the sentence to tell what Kevin will do last.
Draw and color a picture to show what Kevin will do last.

Last _____
_____.

6

9

Set To Sail

Name _____

Follow the directions.
Draw an **X** in each box as the step is completed.

☐ Draw a line to connect the **X**s.
☐ Draw a line to connect the •s.
☐ Color the kite red.
☐ Add a kite tail to the bottom of the kite.
☐ Draw and color five yellow bows on the kite tail.
☐ Draw and color yourself holding on to the kite string.
☐ Draw and color a grassy field.
☐ Color the sun yellow.
☐ Draw and color a rainbow in the sky.
☐ Draw and color a red bird in the sky.
☐ Draw and color a black bird in the sky.
☐ Color the sky blue.

Sailing With Subtraction

Name _____

Solve the problems.
For each answer, circle the digit in the ones column.

Use the circled digits.
Color by the code.

1 = yellow	4 = green
2 = orange	5 = blue
3 = red	6 = purple

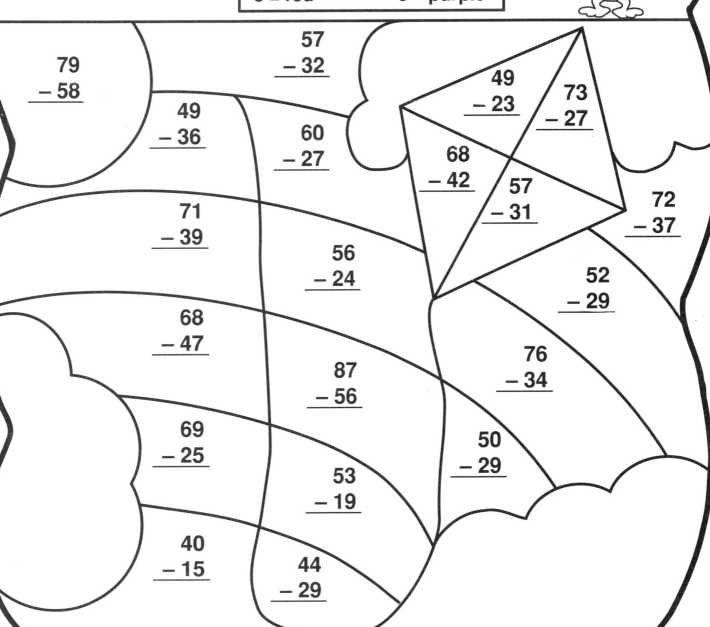

$$79 - 58$$

$$57 - 32$$

$$49 - 36$$

$$60 - 27$$

$$49 - 23$$

$$73 - 27$$

$$68 - 42$$

$$57 - 31$$

$$72 - 37$$

$$71 - 39$$

$$56 - 24$$

$$52 - 29$$

$$68 - 47$$

$$87 - 56$$

$$76 - 34$$

$$69 - 25$$

$$53 - 19$$

$$50 - 29$$

$$40 - 15$$

$$44 - 29$$

Go Fly A Kite!

Name _____

An **idiom** is a group of words with a special meaning.

"**Go fly a kite!**" really means *go away.*

Color the picture that shows the real meaning of the underlined words in each sentence.

Solve the riddle.
Find the letter in each colored picture.
Write the letters in order in the spaces below.

Why couldn't the birthday present answer the phone?
Because it was all ___ ___ ___ ___ ___ ___!

As High As The Sky

Name _____

A **simile** compares two things using the word **like** or **as**.

| like | as |

Example:

Sam's treehouse is as high as the sky.
In this simile the <u>treehouse</u> is compared to the <u>sky</u>.

Complete each simile.
In each kite, draw and color pictures of the two things that are compared.

Katie's <u>hands</u> are as cold as _____.	Amy's <u>eyes</u> are blue like _____.	Jeremy's <u>face</u> turned as red as _____.
A <u>kitten</u> is soft like _____ _____.	An <u>alligator</u> feels as rough as _____.	A new <u>penny</u> is bright like _____.

Measure Up

Name _____

For each kite, cut a piece of string equal to the length shown.
Glue one end of the string at the **X**.

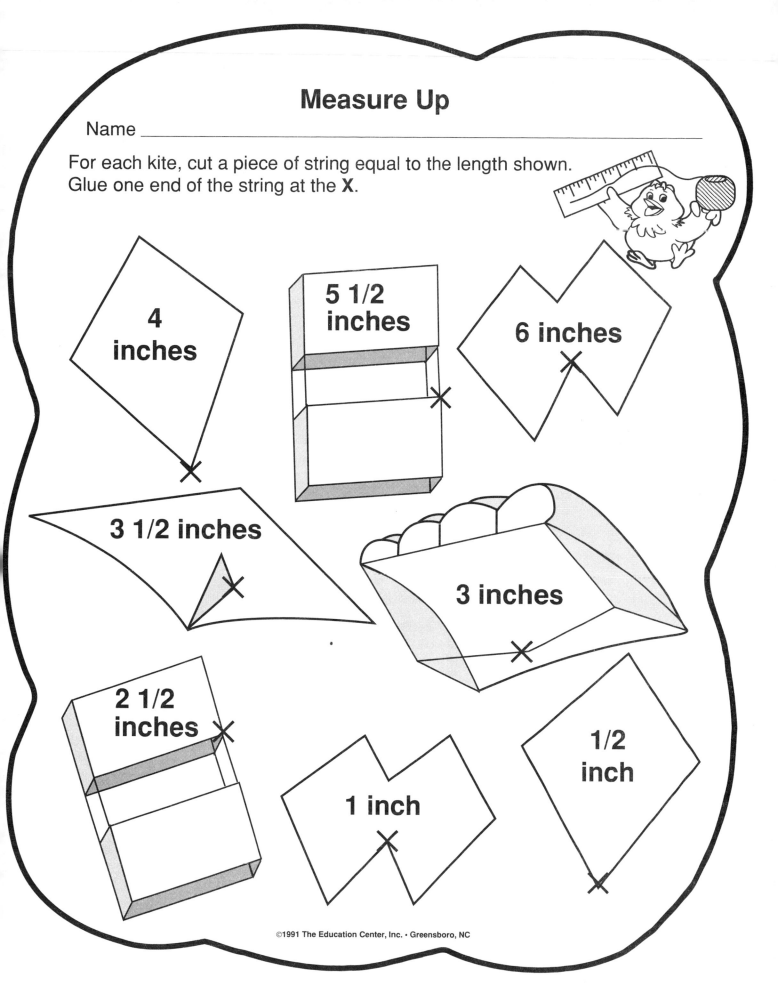

Note To Teacher: Supply each student with approximately 2 1/2 feet of string or yarn to complete this page.

14

A Kite Tale

Name _____

Yesterday I was flying my kite. Suddenly a strong gust of wind came along and lifted me into the air.

©1991 The Education Center, Inc. • Greensboro, NC

Note To Teacher: Have each student write sentences to complete the story, then draw and color himself holding on to the kite string.

15

Puzzling Fliers Pieces
Use with page 8.

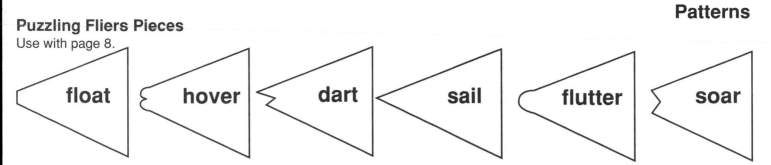

float   hover   dart   sail   flutter   soar

Directions For Covers (continued from page 1):

To make a front cover, use the kite pattern to make a tracer. Trace; then cut out a kite shape from gift wrap or wallpaper scraps. Attach a length of string or yarn to the back of the cutout, near the bottom. Tie tissue paper strips to the "kite string" for bows. Add facial features to the kite; then glue the completed cutout atop the front cover. Gently pull cotton balls into thin wisps; then glue cotton around the kite to resemble clouds.

To make a back cover, duplicate the outline of the front cover on light blue construction paper. Cut out the shape. Staple completed booklet pages between the front and back covers.

Kite Pattern
Use with cover on page 1.

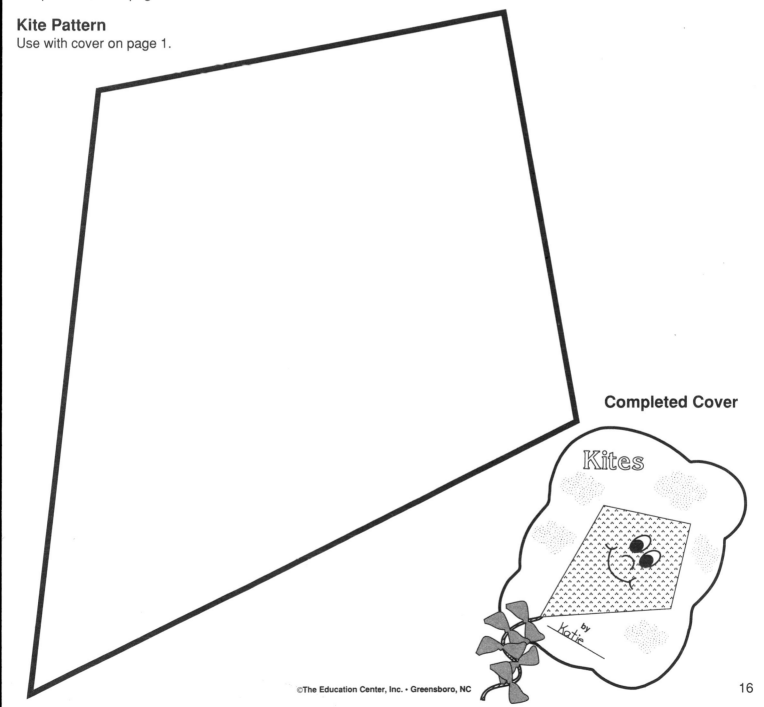

Completed Cover

Completed Cover

Note To Teacher: Duplicate one copy per student on green construction paper; then have students cut them out. See page 31 for directions to complete the covers.

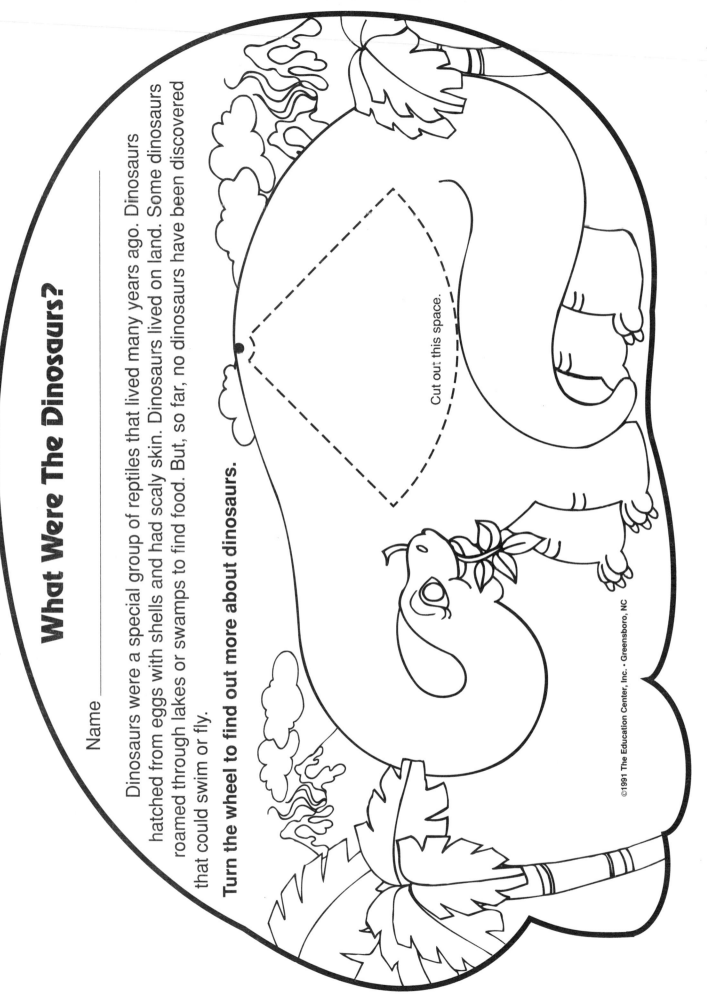

What Were The Dinosaurs?

Name _____

Dinosaurs were a special group of reptiles that lived many years ago. Dinosaurs hatched from eggs with shells and had scaly skin. Dinosaurs lived on land. Some dinosaurs roamed through lakes or swamps to find food. But, so far, no dinosaurs have been discovered that could swim or fly.

Turn the wheel to find out more about dinosaurs.

Cut out this space.

©1991 The Education Center, Inc. • Greensboro, NC

Note To Teacher: To complete this page, have each student cut out the space indicated. Duplicate "Dinosaur Fact Wheel" on page 31 for each student. Have each student color and cut out the wheel, then insert a brad through the dots indicated on this page and on the wheel.

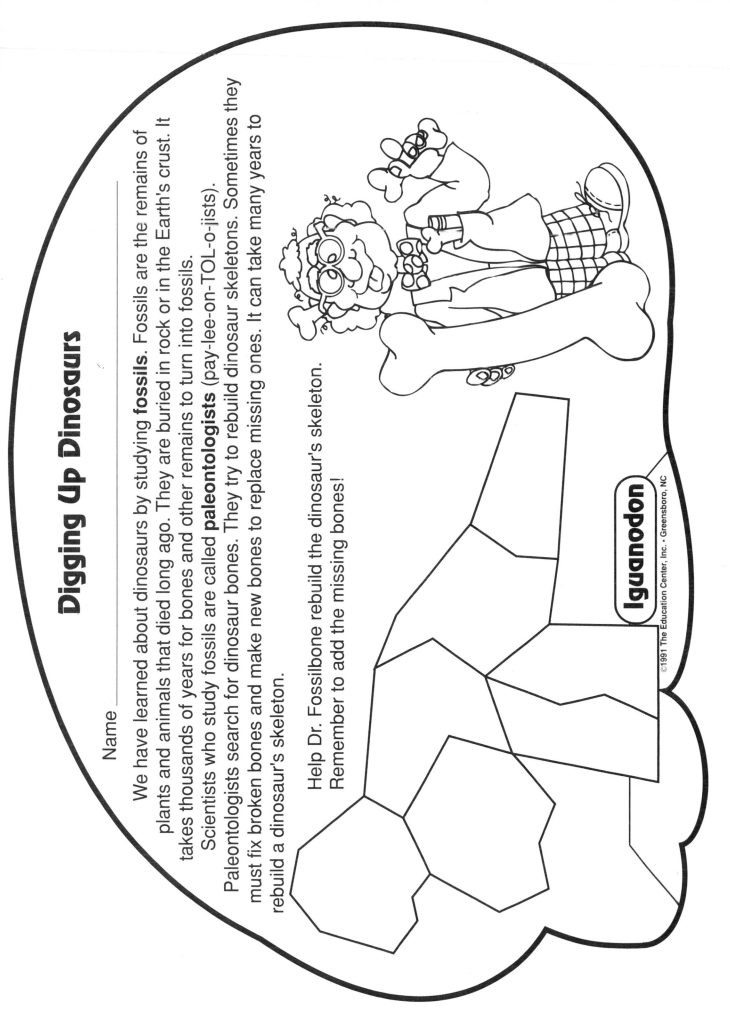

Digging Up Dinosaurs

Name _____

We have learned about dinosaurs by studying **fossils**. Fossils are the remains of plants and animals that died long ago. They are buried in rock or in the Earth's crust. It takes thousands of years for bones and other remains to turn into fossils.

Scientists who study fossils are called **paleontologists** (pay-lee-on-TOL-o-jists). Paleontologists search for dinosaur bones. They try to rebuild dinosaur skeletons. Sometimes they must fix broken bones and make new bones to replace missing ones. It can take many years to rebuild a dinosaur's skeleton.

Help Dr. Fossilbone rebuild the dinosaur's skeleton. Remember to add the missing bones!

Iguanodon

Note To Teacher: Duplicate "Fossil Puzzle Pieces" on page 31 to complete this page.

Dinosaur Detective

Name _____

Dr. Fossilbone is not sure what kind of dinosaur he has found. In his notebook, he wrote what he learned from looking at the bones.
Read his notes.

Look at each dinosaur fact card. If a fact matches Dr. Fossilbone's notes, put a check beside it. If it does not, cross it out.

1. The dinosaur had a long tail.
2. Its length was less than 10 feet.
3. Its teeth were sharp. It was a meat-eater.
4. Its hip joints showed that it was able to walk on two legs.
5. It had two large, sharp claws.

Dinosaur Fact Card
Coelophysis
(see-lo-FISE-iss)

tail: long
length: 10 feet
food: meat
walked on: hind legs or all fours

other fact: It had hollow bones.

Dinosaur Fact Card
Ammosaurus
(AM-uh-SAWR-us)

tail: long
length: 8 feet
food: plants
walked on: hind legs or all fours

other fact: It had a long neck.

Dinosaur Fact Card
Deinonychus
(dine-ON-ik-us)

tail: long
length: 9 feet
food: meat
walked on: hind legs
other fact: It had two large, sharp claws.

Color the dinosaur fact card which has five checks.
It shows the dinosaur Dr. Fossilbone found.

What Happened To The Dinosaurs?

Name _____

No one really knows what happened to the dinosaurs. Many changes happened on Earth. The weather became cooler. Many volcanoes erupted. Rains made dry places wet. Some swamps and seas dried up. Dinosaurs may not have been able to live through these changes. This may have caused them to die out, or become **extinct**. Some people believe the Earth was hit by a huge asteroid.

When the asteroid hit the Earth, a giant dust cloud would have formed. The dust cloud would have blocked out sunlight for several months. Without sunlight, plants could not have grown. Plant-eating dinosaurs would have had no food and died. After a while, meat-eating dinosaurs would have starved, too.

What else could have caused dinosaurs to become extinct?

Write your ideas in Dr. Fossilbone's notebook.

Glue.

Note To Teacher: Duplicate "Dr. Fossilbone's Notebook" on page 31. To complete this page, glue the notebook page in place as indicated before answering the question.

Allosaurus
(AL-uh-SAWR-us)
"Other Lizard"

Name _____

Allosaurus was a meat-eating dinosaur. It had very sharp teeth and claws. Allosaurus was twice as tall as a man. It had a bony bump above each eye. A ridge along the front of its skull made its skull different from the skulls of other meat-eating dinosaurs. The Allosaurus's heavy tail helped it stand up and walk on two legs.

Color Allosaurus.

Circle the correct numbers.

	yes	no
Allosaurus ate meat.	1	2
It had dull teeth.	7	3
A man is taller than Allosaurus.	8	4
It had a bony bump above each eye.	5	2
Allosaurus means "other lizard."	6	8
It walked on four legs.	7	9

1	2	3
4	5	6
7	8	9

Look at the numbers you circled.
Color the matching boxes.

Find the mystery number.
Write it in the blank to complete the Allosaurus fact.

Some of Allosaurus's teeth were _____ inches long!

Ankylosaurus
(ang-kile-uh-SAWR-us)
"Curved Lizard"

Name _____

Ankylosaurus was a plant-eating dinosaur. It looked like an army tank. Bony plates covered its back. There were sharp spines on its sides. Ankylosaurus had a bony knob at the end of its tail. It would hit enemies with its strong tail.

Draw and color some food for Ankylosaurus.
Glue bony plates to its back and tail.

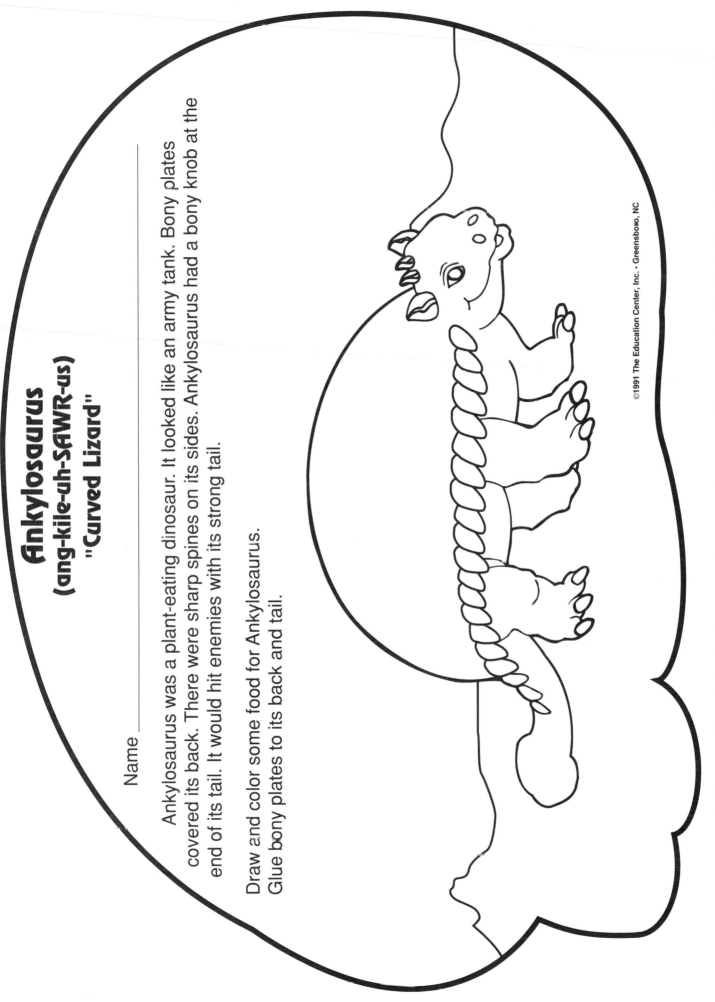

Note To Teacher: Have each child cut or tear fingernail-size pieces from green or brown construction paper or wallpaper scraps. Have him glue the pieces atop Ankylosaurus's back and tail to resemble bony plates.

Apatosaurus
(ah-PAT-uh-SAWR-us)
"Deceptive Lizard"

Name _____

Apatosaurus was a huge dinosaur. When it walked, the ground rumbled like thunder. It had very small, weak teeth. It probably swallowed most of the plants it ate whole. Apatosaurus often stood in the water so it would be safe from its enemies. This dinosaur used to be known as *Brontosaurus*.

Help Apatosaurus stay safe. Make a lake for it.

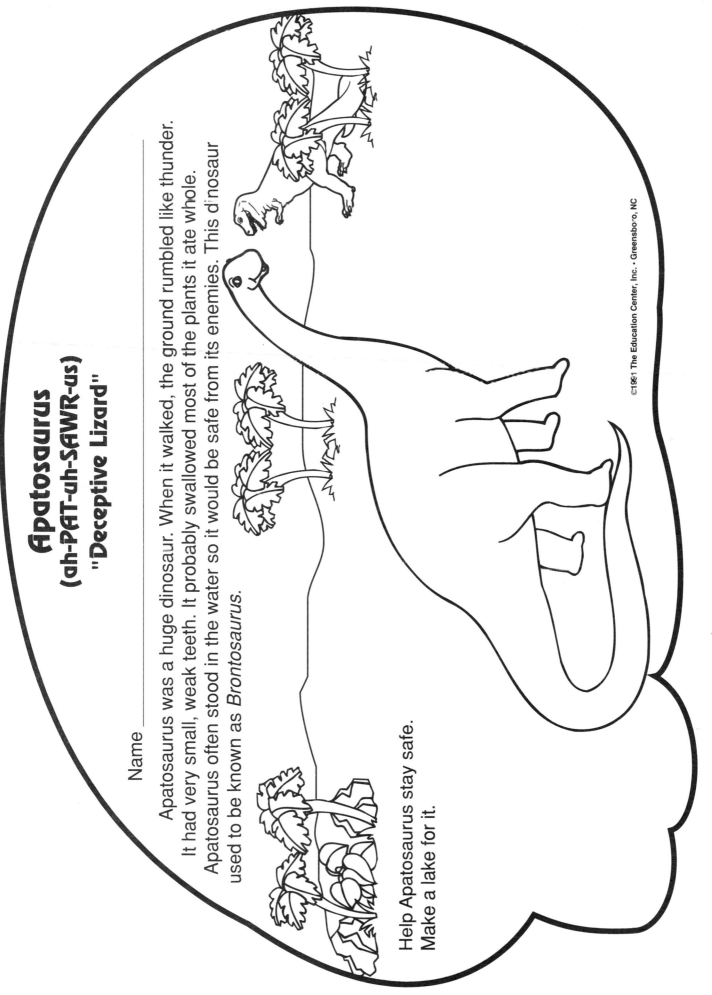

Note To Teacher: Have each child cut or tear thumb-size pieces of blue cellophane, plastic wrap, construction paper, or tissue paper; then have him glue the pieces around Apatosaurus to resemble a lake.

24

Brachiosaurus
(BRAK-ee-uh-SAWR-us)
"Arm Lizard"

Name _____

This giant dinosaur had four strong legs and a long neck. It ate leaves from the tops of trees. It was so tall it could have looked over a four-story building. Brachiosaurus spent a lot of time in deep water. Scientists think it hid from its enemies in the water. It could stay out of sight by breathing through the nostrils on top of its head.

For a long time, Brachiosaurus was the biggest known dinosaur. Now the bones of two other dinosaurs have been found. These dinosaurs may have been even bigger! Scientists have nicknamed these dinosaurs *Supersaurus* and *Ultrasaurus*.

Show how Brachiosaurus might have hidden from its enemies.

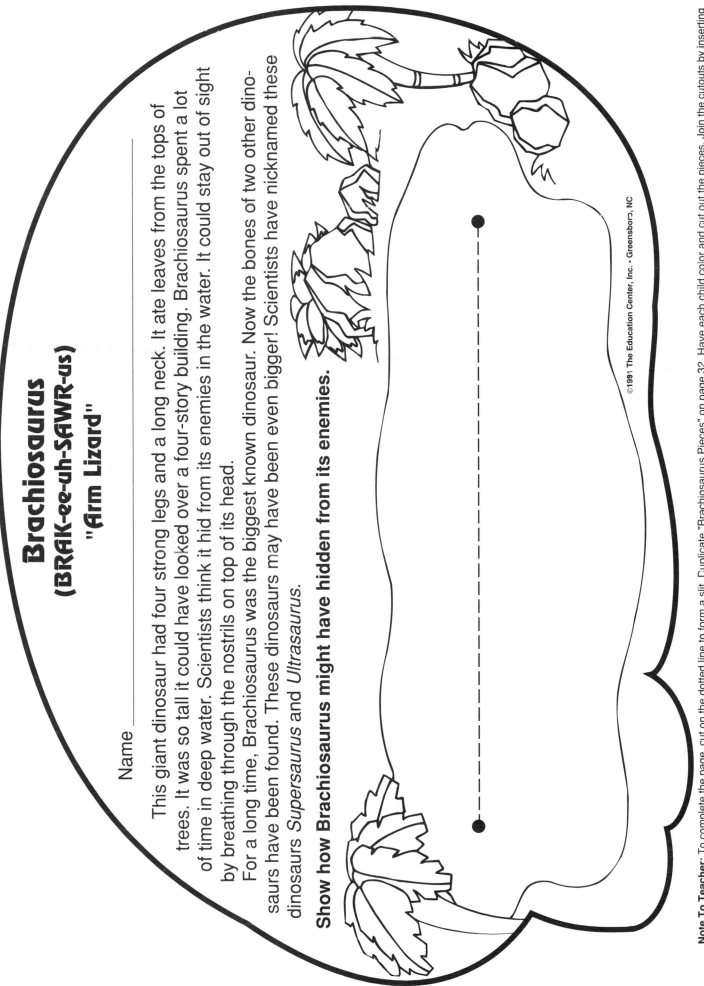

©1991 The Education Center, Inc. • Greensboro, NC

Stegosaurus
(STEG-uh-SAWR-us)
"Roof Lizard"

Name _____

Stegosaurus was as long as two cars. But it might have had the smallest brain of any dinosaur. Its brain was only the size of a walnut! It had no teeth in the front of its mouth. The front of its mouth was a toothless "beak." It probably ate mostly soft plants. Stegosaurus had bony plates on its back. Its tail had four, long spikes at the end. It used its tail to protect itself.

Fill in the blanks.
Use the words on the bony plates.

1. Stegosaurus was as long as two _____.

2. It had a _____ brain.

3. It ate _____.

4. Stegosaurus had _____ plates on its back.

5. The _____ on its tail helped it protect itself.

Add spikes to Stegosaurus's tail.

(words on the bony plates: spikes, cars, small, plants, bony)

Note To Teacher: Provide two toothpicks for each student. To complete this page, have each child break his two toothpicks in half. At each dot, glue a toothpick half atop the tail to resemble a spike.

Triceratops
(try-SAIR-uh-tops)
"Three-horned Face"

Name _____

Triceratops was a plant-eating dinosaur. Scientists think this horned dinosaur lived in herds. It had a bony frill around the back of its head. It also had a long horn over each eye and a shorter one on its nose. Triceratops used its horns to protect itself. It may also have used its horns to fight other Triceratopses when it battled to become the herd leader.

Circle the number below each correct answer.

Triceratops ate _____.

rocks	plants	bones
7	8	9

It had _____ horns.

four	three	two
10	11	12

Triceratops lived in a _____.

house	lake	herd
7	8	9

It used its horns to _____.

eat	jump	fight
10	11	12

The horns above Triceratops's eyes were up to _____ inches long.

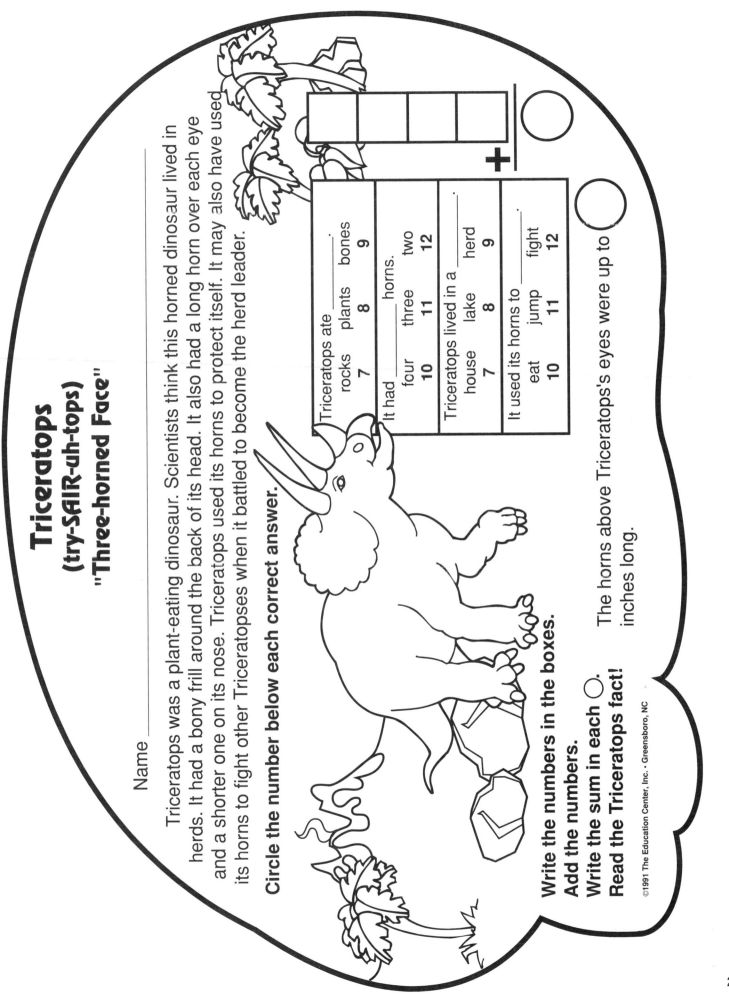

Write the numbers in the boxes.
Add the numbers.
Write the sum in each ◯.
Read the Triceratops fact!

©1991 The Education Center, Inc. • Greensboro, NC

27

Tyrannosaurus
(tye-RAN-uh-SAWR-us)
"Tyrant Lizard"

Name _____

Tyrannosaurus was the largest meat-eating dinosaur. It had a huge head. Its teeth were as sharp as knives. Some of its teeth were over six inches long. Tyrannosaurus walked on its strong back legs. It used its small front claws for holding food. This dinosaur was a great hunter.

Use the ruler.
Measure to find five things that are about the same length as the Tyrannosaurus Tooth Ruler. Write them in the spaces below.

1. _____
2. _____
3. _____
4. _____
5. _____

Color Tyrannosaurus.

Slit.

Note To Teacher: To complete this page, cut on the dotted lines to form a slit. Duplicate "Tyrannosaurus Pieces" on page 32 on construction paper for each child. Have each child cut out and glue the pocket to the back of the page as indicated. Cut out the ruler. Store the ruler in the pocket.

28

Mistaken Identities

Name _____

Not all prehistoric animals were dinosaurs. Some non-dinosaur animals flew. These flying reptiles were called **pterosaurs** (TAIR-uh-sawrz). Another group of non-dinosaur animals lived in the water. They were called **plesiosaurs** (PLEE-zee-uh-sawrz). **Pteranodon** (te-RAN-a-don) was a pterosaur. It had a long, toothless beak. It had a bony crest on the back of its head. Pteranodon probably did not flap its wings and fly. It may have just glided through the air. Pteranodon ate fish. It may have caught fish while gliding across the water.

Slit. Insert one wing.

Color the prehistoric scene. See how far your Pteranodon glider can glide.

©1991 The Education Center, Inc. • Greensboro, NC

Peloneustes was a plesiosaur.

Note To Teacher: To complete this page, cut on the dotted line to form a slit. Duplicate a copy of "Pteranodon Glider" on page 32 for each student. Have each student color and cut out the glider. Fold it in half along the center line. Then fold down each wing as indicated. Glue the head and body portions of the glider together. Store the glider by inserting one of its wings through the slit.

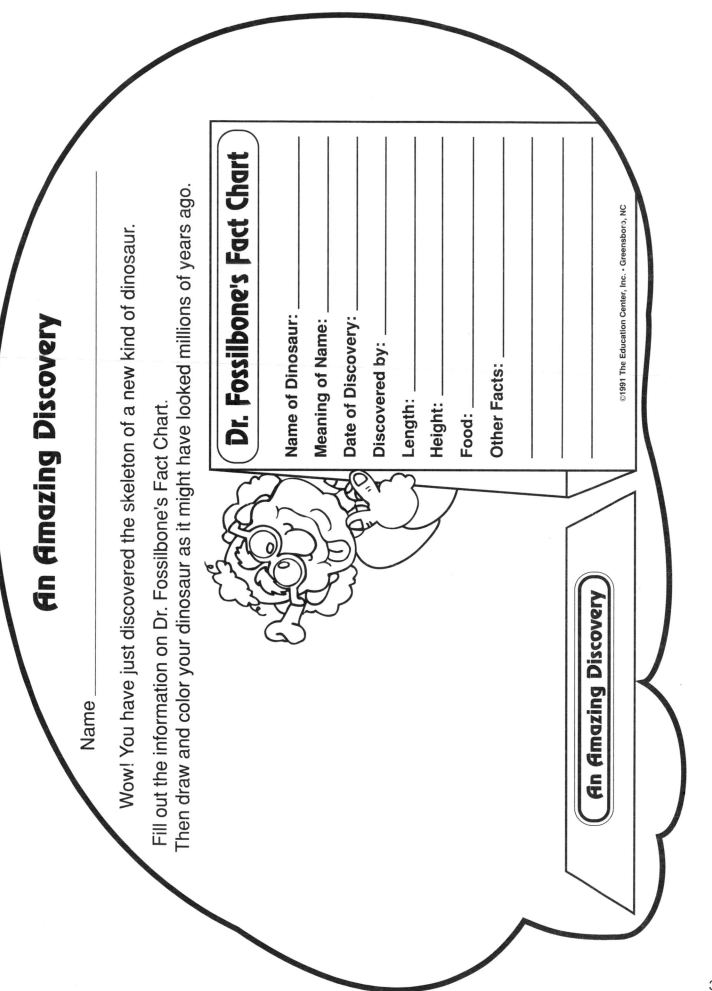

An Amazing Discovery

Name _____

Wow! You have just discovered the skeleton of a new kind of dinosaur.

Fill out the information on Dr. Fossilbone's Fact Chart.
Then draw and color your dinosaur as it might have looked millions of years ago.

Dr. Fossilbone's Fact Chart

Name of Dinosaur: _____

Meaning of Name: _____

Date of Discovery: _____

Discovered by: _____

Length: _____

Height: _____

Food: _____

Other Facts: _____
_____

An Amazing Discovery

Dinosaur Fact Wheel
Use with page 18.

Fossil Puzzle Pieces
Use with page 19.

Patterns

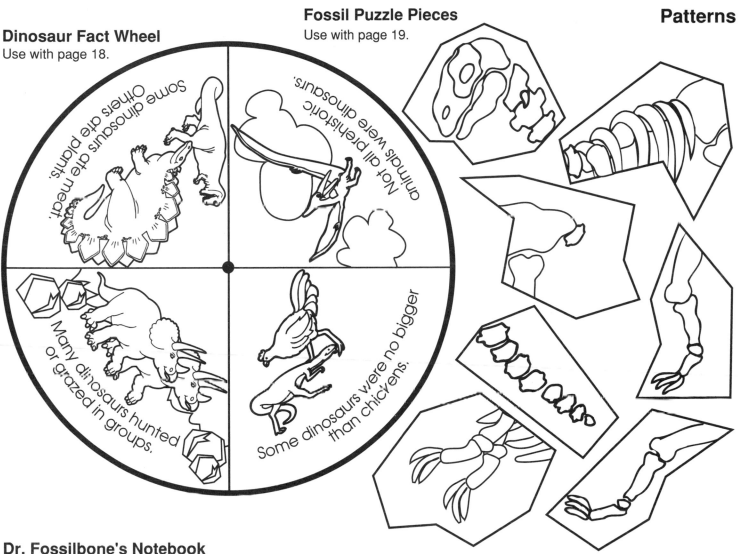

Dr. Fossilbone's Notebook
Use with page 21.

Date: ___ / ___ / ___

How Dinosaurs Became Extinct

Directions For Covers (continued from page 17):

To make a front cover, use the bony plates patterns to make tracers. Trace each pattern onto dark green or brown construction paper six times. Cut out the shapes. Glue the large cutouts atop the center of the dinosaur's back so they slightly overlap. Attach medium and small cutouts to each side of the large plates as shown on page 17. For spikes, glue four narrow white construction paper or Styrofoam strips to the end of the tail. Attach wiggle eyes or eyes cut from construction paper scraps.

To make a back cover, duplicate the outline of the front cover on green construction paper. Cut out the shape. Staple the completed booklet pages between the front and back covers.

Bony Plates Patterns
Use with page 17.

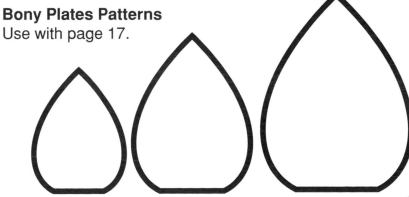

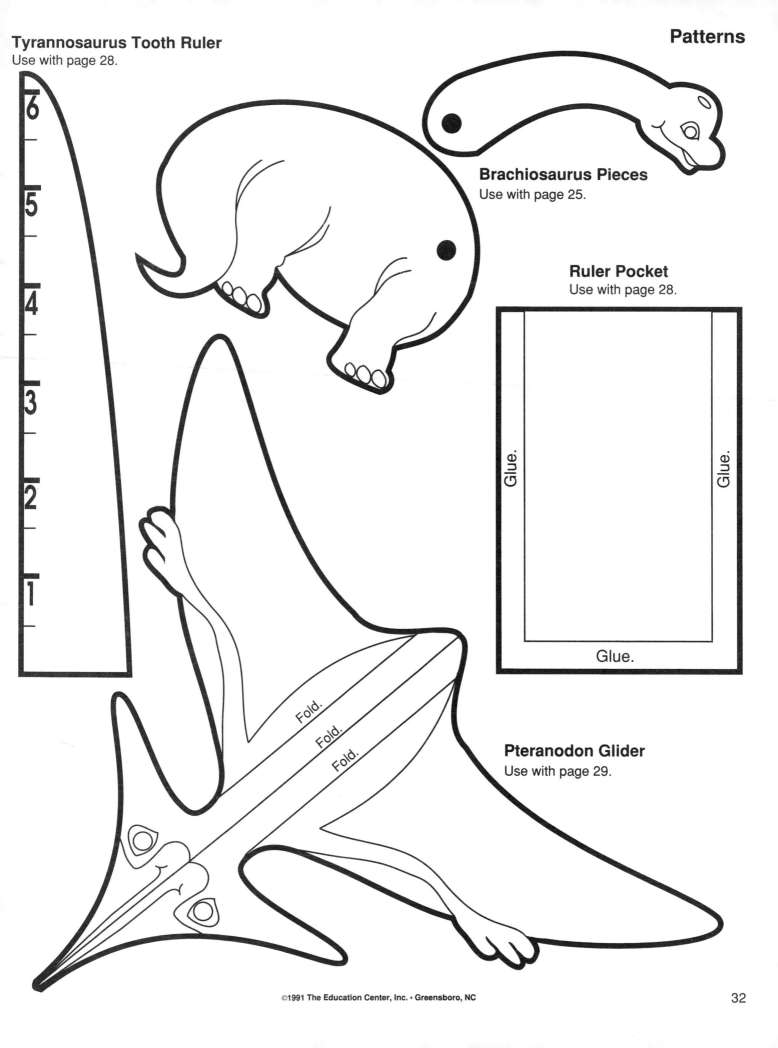

Tyrannosaurus Tooth Ruler
Use with page 28.

6
5
4
3
2
1

Patterns

Brachiosaurus Pieces
Use with page 25.

Ruler Pocket
Use with page 28.

Glue.

Glue.

Glue.

Fold.
Fold.
Fold.

Pteranodon Glider
Use with page 29.

Note To Teacher: Duplicate one copy per student on green construction paper; then have students cut them out. See page 37 for directions to complete the covers.

Frogs

by _____

33

Froggie "Phun"

Name _____

The sound you hear at the beginning of my name is spelled with the letter **f**. The letters **ff**, **gh**, and **ph** can also spell this sound.

Felix

Fill in the missing letters to complete each word.
Color the matching lily pad below.

flu_____y
cou_____ed
al_____abet
rou_____
tele_____one

tou_____
ele_____ant
bu_____alo
whi_____

gra_____
stu_____ing
mu_____in
lau_____ter
enou_____

gh

ff

ph

gh

gh

ff

ff

ph

ph

ph

ph

ff

gh

ff

gh

Find the lily pad that is not colored.
Color it yellow.
Color Felix, too!

34

Fraction Frolic

Name _____

Follow the directions to color each set.

- Draw spots on three-fourths of the frogs.
- Color the spots yellow.
- Color one-fourth of the frogs light green.
- Color three-fourths of the frogs dark green.

- Draw a lily on five-sixths of the lily pads.
- Color the center of each lily yellow.
- Color the lily pads green.

- Color three-eighths of the dragonflies green.
- Color five-eighths of the dragonflies blue.

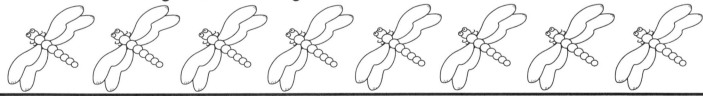

- Draw lily pads on two-thirds of the ponds.
- Color the lily pads green.
- Color the ponds blue.

Let's Play Leapfrog!

Name _____

3 X 4 = 12

Use the product pointer and the number lines.
Find the products.

7 X 3 = _____
6 X 4 = _____
1 X 3 = _____
4 X 4 = _____
0 X 4 = _____

3 X 3 = _____
7 X 4 = _____
2 X 3 = _____
6 X 3 = _____
1 X 4 = _____

2 X 4 = _____
9 X 4 = _____
8 X 3 = _____
0 X 4 = _____
4 X 3 = _____

9 X 3 = _____
8 X 4 = _____
5 X 4 = _____
5 X 3 = _____
3 X 4 = _____

X 3

0   3   6   9   12   15   18   21   24   27   30   33   36

X 4

0   4   8   12   16   20   24   28   32   36

Glue.

Glue.

Glue.

Glue.

©1991 The Education Center, Inc. • Greensboro, NC

frog
Use with
booklet cover
on page 33.

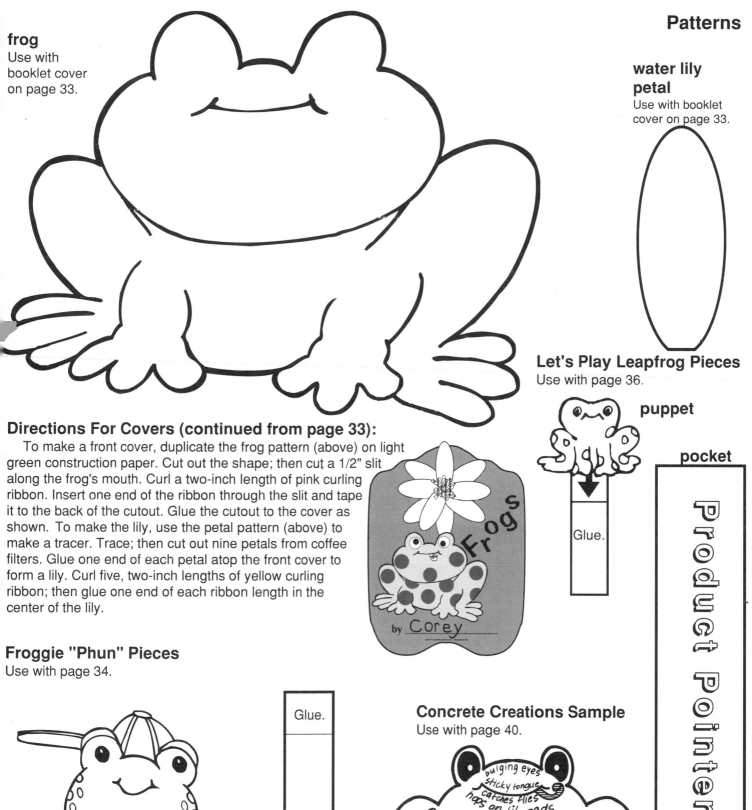

water lily petal
Use with booklet cover on page 33.

Let's Play Leapfrog Pieces
Use with page 36.

puppet

pocket

Glue.

Product Pointer

Directions For Covers (continued from page 33):

To make a front cover, duplicate the frog pattern (above) on light green construction paper. Cut out the shape; then cut a 1/2" slit along the frog's mouth. Curl a two-inch length of pink curling ribbon. Insert one end of the ribbon through the slit and tape it to the back of the cutout. Glue the cutout to the cover as shown. To make the lily, use the petal pattern (above) to make a tracer. Trace; then cut out nine petals from coffee filters. Glue one end of each petal atop the front cover to form a lily. Curl five, two-inch lengths of yellow curling ribbon; then glue one end of each ribbon length in the center of the lily.

Frogs
by Corey

Froggie "Phun" Pieces
Use with page 34.

Phil

Glue.

Glue.

Concrete Creations Sample
Use with page 40.

bulging eyes
sticky tongue
catches flies
hops on lily pads
with its long legs
eggs hatch into little tadpoles
croak croak
hops, jumps, leaps, swims

Leapin' Lily Pads

Name _____

Match an entry word frog to each pair of guide words.
Color and cut out the frogs.
Glue a frog to each lily pad at the ● .

lost—lunch

flight—four

lime—lonely

face—fear

feed—fig

led—light

friend—fun

lace—learn

fir—flew

fox—freeze

38

Note To Teacher: Duplicate "Jumpin' Jamboree Pieces" on page 47 to complete this page. Have each student color and cut out the ribbons, then glue them atop the winning frogs.

Jumpin' Jamboree

Name _____

Add and subtract to complete the table.
Use the table to answer the questions below.

Jumpin' Jamboree Results

(Each jump was measured in inches.)

jumper	round 1	round 2	round 3	total
Felix	32	33	30	95
Freddie	36	35	34	
Francine	33	29	31	
Frieda	34	32		104

Which frog jumped the farthest in round 1? _____

Which frog jumped the farthest in round 3? _____

How far did Freddie jump on his second try? _____

Which round was Francine's best? _____

Which round was Frieda's worst? _____

Which frog jumped 30 inches in round 3? _____

What was the length of the shortest jump in the contest? _____

Concrete Creations

Name _____

A **concrete poem** is written in a special shape.
The words in the poem tell about its shape.

Write about frogs in each lily pad.
Use the words in the lily pads to write a concrete poem about frogs in the
 frog shape below.

How Frogs Look and Feel

bulging eyes

Things Frogs Do

croak at night

Fun Frog Facts

live in ponds

"Pond-ering" Pronouns

Name _____

Use the pronouns on Felix's spots.
Replace the underlined word or words in each sentence.
Write the pronoun on the matching lily pad.
Then color the spot.

1. _____
2. _____
3. _____
4. _____
5. _____

6. _____
7. _____
8. _____
9. _____
10. _____

1. <u>Felix and I</u> went to the pond.
2. Frieda and Francine wanted to play with <u>Felix and me</u>.
3. <u>Francine</u> hopped to a lily pad.
4. <u>The lily pad</u> was in the middle of the pond.
5. <u>Felix</u> hopped onto another lily pad.
6. <u>Frieda and Francine</u> wanted to play leapfrog.
7. It was fun to jump over <u>Frieda and Francine</u>.
8. We all cheered when Francine jumped over <u>Felix</u>.
9. The jump was a long one for <u>Francine</u>.
10. "<u>Felix and you</u> are good sports," said Francine.

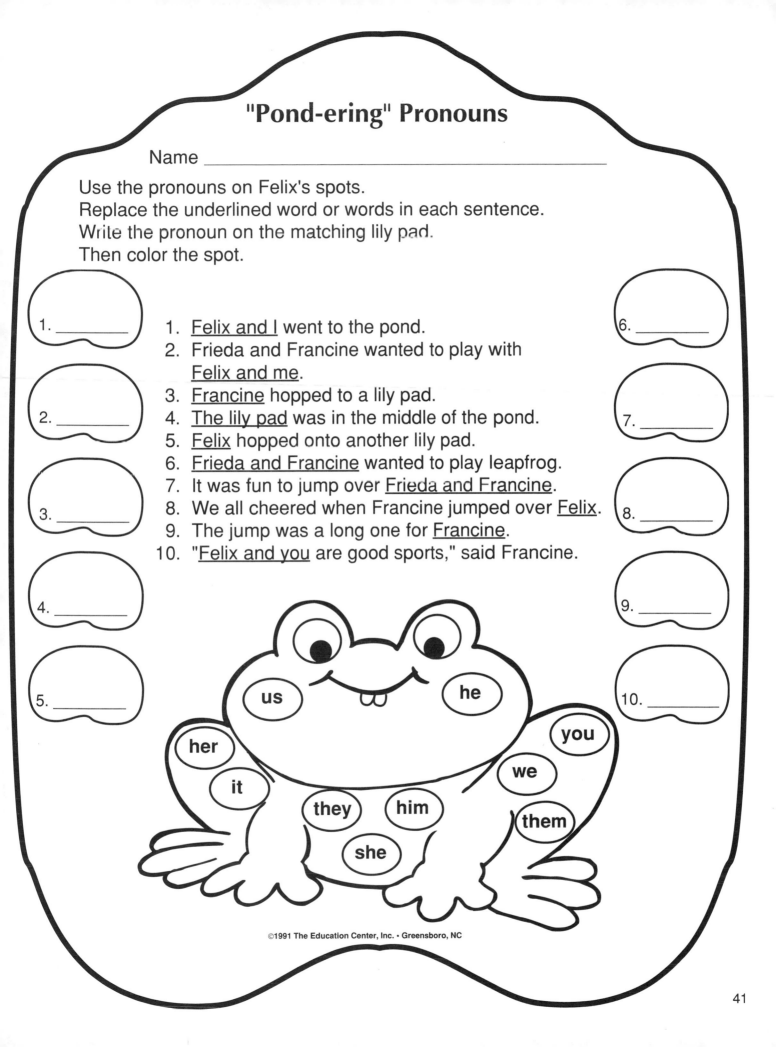

us   he
her   you
it   we
they   him   them
she

41

Note To Teacher: Duplicate "Catchin' Flies Pennant" on page 47. To complete this page, color and cut out the pennant. Fold and tape the pennant to a toothpick; then insert the toothpick through the dot on the hand of the winning team's player. Secure the pennant by taping the toothpick to the back of the page.

Catchin' Flies

Name _____

Solve each problem.
Use the color code to **outline** the fly balls.

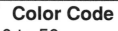

Color Code	
0 to 50	= red
51 to 99	= blue

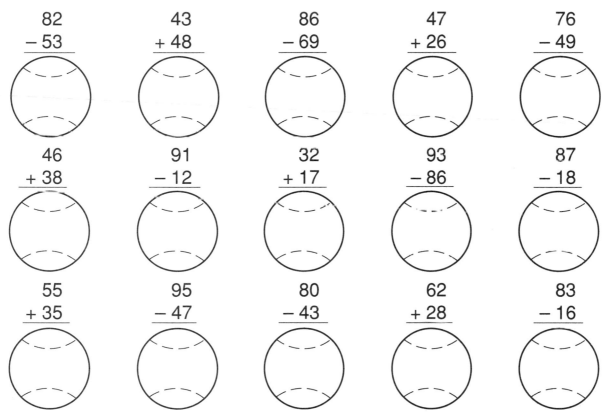

$$\begin{array}{r} 82 \\ -53 \\ \hline \end{array}$$

$$\begin{array}{r} 43 \\ +48 \\ \hline \end{array}$$

$$\begin{array}{r} 86 \\ -69 \\ \hline \end{array}$$

$$\begin{array}{r} 47 \\ +26 \\ \hline \end{array}$$

$$\begin{array}{r} 76 \\ -49 \\ \hline \end{array}$$

$$\begin{array}{r} 46 \\ +38 \\ \hline \end{array}$$

$$\begin{array}{r} 91 \\ -12 \\ \hline \end{array}$$

$$\begin{array}{r} 32 \\ +17 \\ \hline \end{array}$$

$$\begin{array}{r} 93 \\ -86 \\ \hline \end{array}$$

$$\begin{array}{r} 87 \\ -18 \\ \hline \end{array}$$

$$\begin{array}{r} 55 \\ +35 \\ \hline \end{array}$$

$$\begin{array}{r} 95 \\ -47 \\ \hline \end{array}$$

$$\begin{array}{r} 80 \\ -43 \\ \hline \end{array}$$

$$\begin{array}{r} 62 \\ +28 \\ \hline \end{array}$$

$$\begin{array}{r} 83 \\ -16 \\ \hline \end{array}$$

Fly balls outlined in blue were caught by the blue team.
Fly balls outlined in red were caught by the red team.

Count the fly balls each team caught.
Write the final score on the scoreboard.

Final Score

red   blue

42

A Handsome Prince

Name _____

Princess Pamela's prince has turned into a frog!
To find him:
- Read each clue.
- Draw an X atop each frog that **cannot** be the prince.
- Color the frog that is the prince.

Clues
1. The prince's name starts with the letter *F*.
2. The prince is sitting on a lily pad.
3. The prince is not wearing a bow tie.
4. The prince has spots.

Felix

Fergus

Frisco

Gus

Frank

Freddie

Poof! The prince has returned.
Draw and color the prince beside Princess Pamela.

Note To Teacher: Duplicate "Hop To It! Pieces" on page 47. To complete this page, color and cut out the lily pads before gluing them in place.

Hop To It!

Name _____

Glue each lily pad inside the correct pond.

Noun Pond
No verbs allowed.
People, places, and things only!

Verb Pond
This pond is hoppin' with action!

"Toad-ally" Awesome

Name _____

Make new words by writing the suffixes **er**, **ly**, **ful**, and **less** in the blanks.
Then color by the code.

Code: er   = **blue**
ly   = **dark green**
ful   = **orange**
less = **light green**

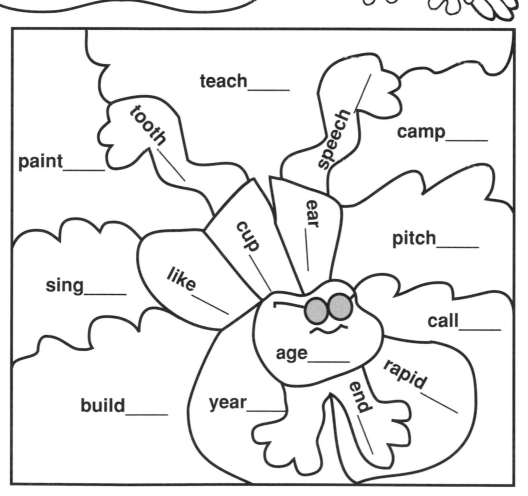

teach____

tooth____

speech____

camp____

paint____

ear____

cup____

pitch____

like____

sing____

call____

age____

build____

year____

end____

rapid____

It's Pouring!

Name _____

Rrremember…

2 cups = 1 pint

2 pints = 1 quart

4 quarts = 1 gallon

Read each sentence.
Circle the correct letter.

		Yes	No
1.	A pint is more than a cup.	a	e
2.	A quart is more than a gallon.	n	m
3.	Two pints are equal to one gallon.	b	c
4.	A cup is less than a quart.	e	o
5.	Two cups equal one quart.	k	f
6.	A gallon is more than a pint.	h	b
7.	Four quarts equal one pint.	u	i
8.	Three cups are more than one pint.	s	w
9.	Three pints are less than one quart.	g	t
10.	Five quarts are more than one gallon.	y	p

Solve the riddle.
Write the circled letters in the blanks below.

Why do frogs make such good outfielders?

B __ __ __ u __ __ __ __ __ __ __ __ __ __
 4 3 1   8 4   9 6 4 10   3 1 9 3 6

__ o __ __ n __ __ l __ __ __.
 8   2 1 10   5 7 4 8

Leapin' Lily Pads Pieces
Use with page 38.

life

lazy

lucky

fever

frame

fly

loaf

fruit

flavor

family

Jumpin' Jamboree Pieces
Use with page 39.

Longest Jump 1st

Overall Winner 1st

Catchin' Flies Pennant
Use with page 42.

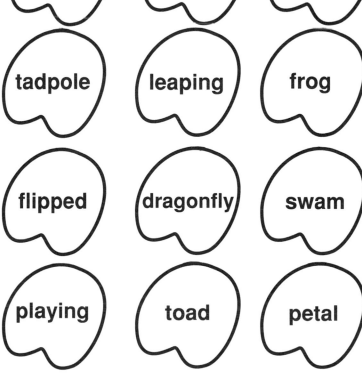

Fold and tape.

Fly-catchin' CHAMPS

Hop To It Pieces
Use with page 44.

jumping

lily pad

croaked

tadpole

leaping

frog

flipped

dragonfly

swam

playing

toad

petal

©1991 The Education Center, Inc. • Greensboro, NC

©1991 The Education Center, Inc. • Greensboro, NC

Patterns

To complete the cover on page 48:

1. Color the butterfly with crayons or markers; then cut it out. Use it to trace a back cover on construction paper if you wish.
2. Punch holes where indicated on the butterfly's wings.
3. Cut two 17-inch pieces of ribbon. Thread each piece through the holes of one wing. Tape the ends of the ribbon pieces to the back.
4. Cut slits along the dotted lines. Fold the hands up slightly.
5. Duplicate the nameplate below on construction paper.
6. Color, label, and cut out the nameplate.
7. Glue the nameplate just below the butterfly's hands (see illustration).
8. Cut a black or brown pipe cleaner in half. Bend one end of each piece slightly to make a knob; then tape the pipe cleaner pieces to the back of the butterfly's head to make antennae.

Nameplate Pattern

See page 50 for instructions on using the ruler and pocket patterns.

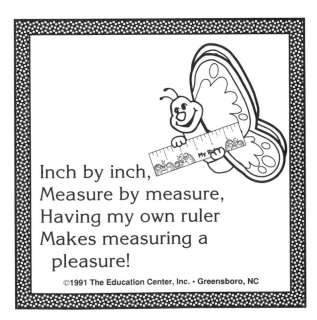

Pocket Pattern

49

Name:

_____

Big ones, small ones—you'll find butterflies in almost every part of the world. They live in forests, jungles, deserts, and even the freezing Arctic. Butterflies live any place where trees and plants grow. That is because butterflies eat plants for food.

Butterflies come in many different sizes. The largest butterfly is about 11 inches across! Other butterflies are less than one inch across.

Directions: Measure the wingspan of each butterfly. Measure from dot to dot. Write your answer in the blank. Then color the butterflies.

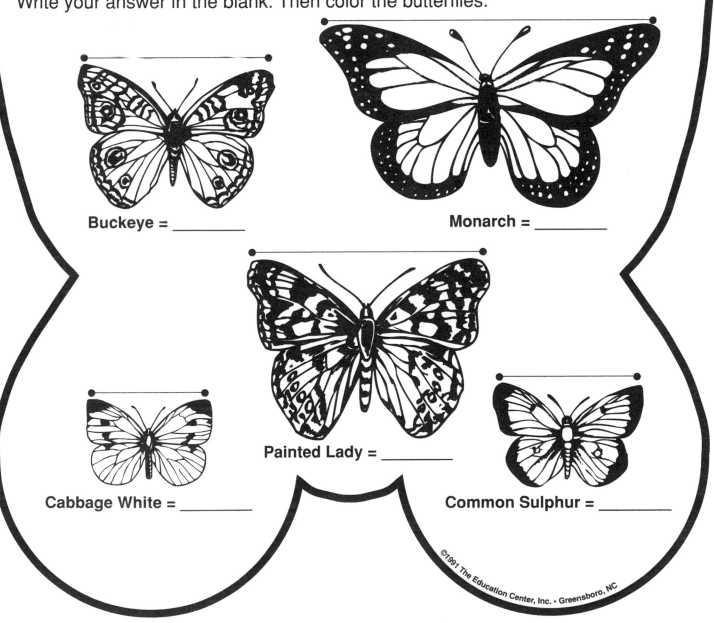

Buckeye = _____

Monarch = _____

Painted Lady = _____

Cabbage White = _____

Common Sulphur = _____

©1991 The Education Center, Inc. • Greensboro, NC

Note To Teacher: Duplicate the ruler and pocket patterns on page 49 on construction paper for each child. Have the child tape the pocket to the back of the page and store the ruler inside.

Name:

_____

A butterfly is an insect. Its body has three main parts: the *head,* the *thorax,* and the *abdomen.*

A butterfly's head has two very big eyes, a pair of antennae, and a long tongue. Each eye is made of thousands of little eyes! The antennae are club-shaped. The butterfly uses its antennae to smell and touch. The tongue is really a long tube. The butterfly uses it to suck up water or nectar from flowers.

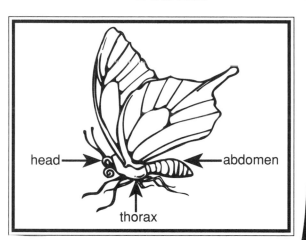

Directions: Label the parts of the butterfly's head: **eyes, antennae, tongue.**

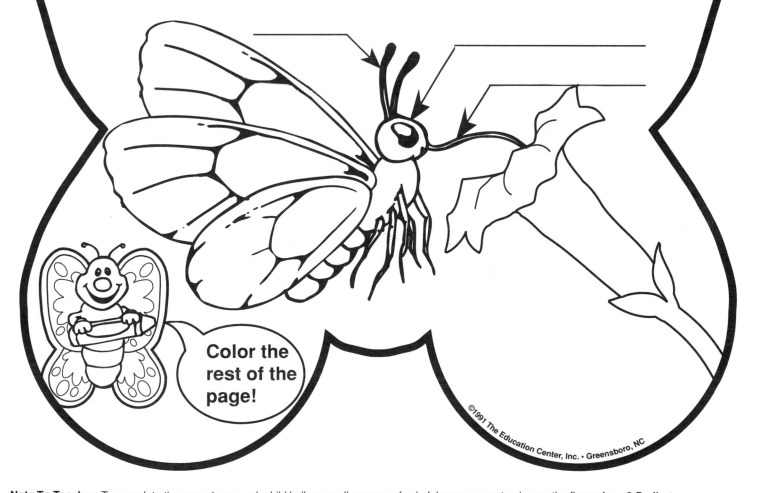

Color the rest of the page!

©1991 The Education Center, Inc. • Greensboro, NC

Note To Teacher: To complete the page, have each child ball up small squares of colorful crepe paper to glue on the flower for a 3-D effect. Glue green tissue paper balls to the stem and sepals.

The Thorax And Abdomen

The *thorax* is the middle of the butterfly's body. Two pairs of wings are attached to the thorax. The wings are covered with many tiny scales. The scales give the butterfly its beautiful colors. Three pairs of legs are also attached to the thorax.

The *abdomen* is the biggest part of the butterfly's body. There are holes on the sides of the abdomen. The butterfly breathes through these holes.

thorax →

breathing holes

abdomen

Write each letter in the correct blank. Then color the butterfly's body.

1. _____ thorax
2. _____ wings
3. _____ number of wings
4. _____ number of legs
5. _____ abdomen
6. _____ covering on wings

a. scales
b. attached to thorax
c. six
d. largest part of body
e. four
f. middle part of body

©1991 The Education Center, Inc. • Greensboro, NC

Note To Teacher: To complete this page, see the wings pattern and the instructions on page 53.

To complete page 52:

1. Duplicate the wings pattern on white paper for each child.
2. Have students color the wings using the *pointillism* technique: use a fine-tipped marker to cover each enclosed area with many tiny dots spaced close together (see illustration).
3. Cut out the wings. Fold on the dotted line of the tab.
4. Cut a slit on page 52 where indicated.
5. Insert the wings' tab in the slit; tape the tab to the back of the page.
6. To keep the wings upright, place a small dot of glue on the back of the top of the wings. Gently press it on the page.

Example

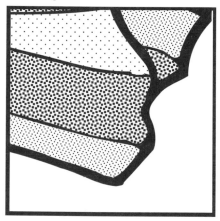

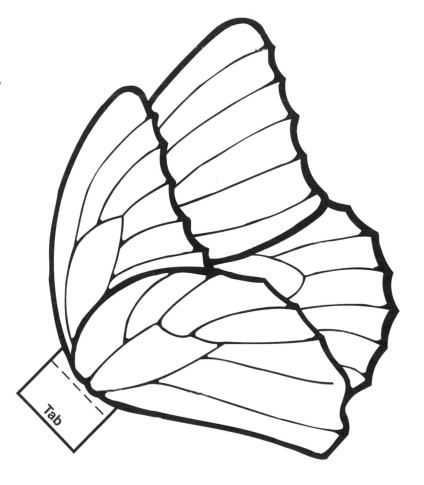

See the instructions for using these patterns on page 54.

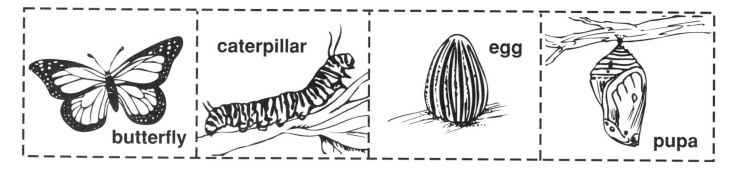

butterfly   caterpillar   egg   pupa

Name:

_____

**Lots
Of
Changes**

How is a butterfly born? It happens in four different parts, or *stages.* The butterfly changes in each stage.

A butterfly begins life as an **egg**. The egg hatches into a **caterpillar**. The caterpillar turns into a **pupa**. One day a **butterfly** comes out of the pupa.

**Color the pictures.
Paste each picture in the correct box.
Then color Flutter!**

©1991 The Education Center, Inc. • Greensboro, NC

Note To Teacher: Duplicate the patterns on page 53 for each student to color and paste on this page. If desired, provide a pair of small wiggle eyes to glue to the butterfly.

54

Name: _____

All butterflies begin life as eggs. Most butterflies lay their eggs on leaves. The eggs are very small. Each egg is only about the size of a pin head! Most eggs are green or yellow, but some can be orange or red.

The eggs of some butterflies hatch in a few days. Other butterfly eggs may take months to hatch.

Directions: Each animal listed in the chart also starts life as an egg. In the chart, write how each animal is like and unlike a butterfly. Use your imagination!

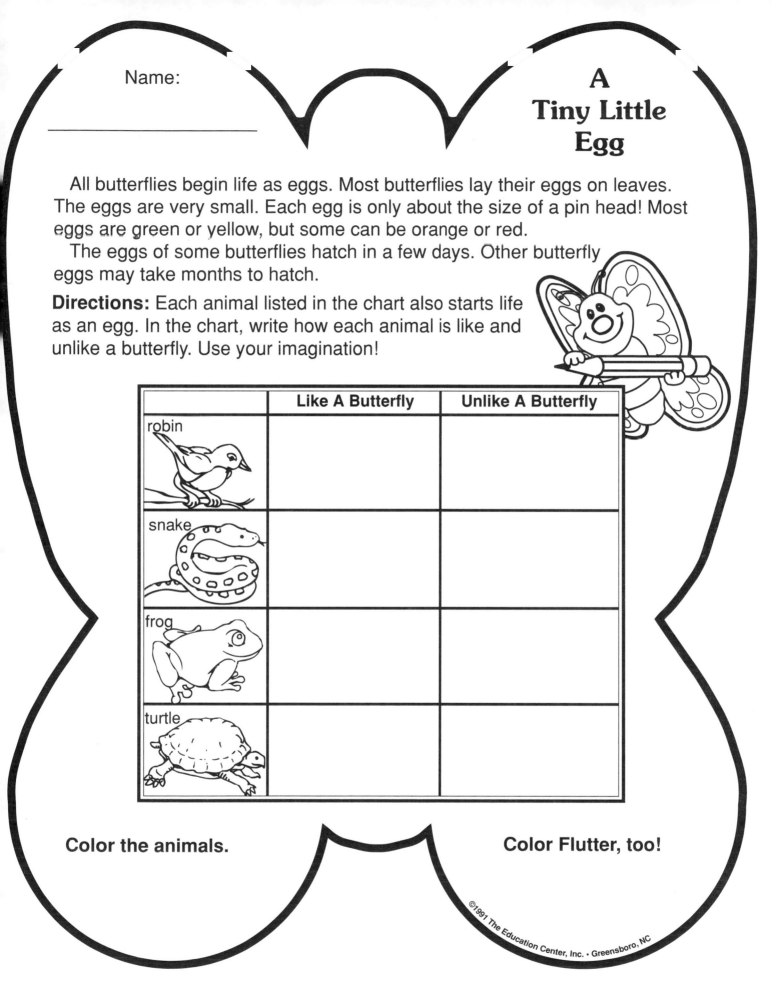

	Like A Butterfly	Unlike A Butterfly
robin		
snake		
frog		
turtle		

Color the animals.   **Color Flutter, too!**

©1991 The Education Center, Inc. • Greensboro, NC

55

Name:

_____

Creeping, Crawling Caterpillar

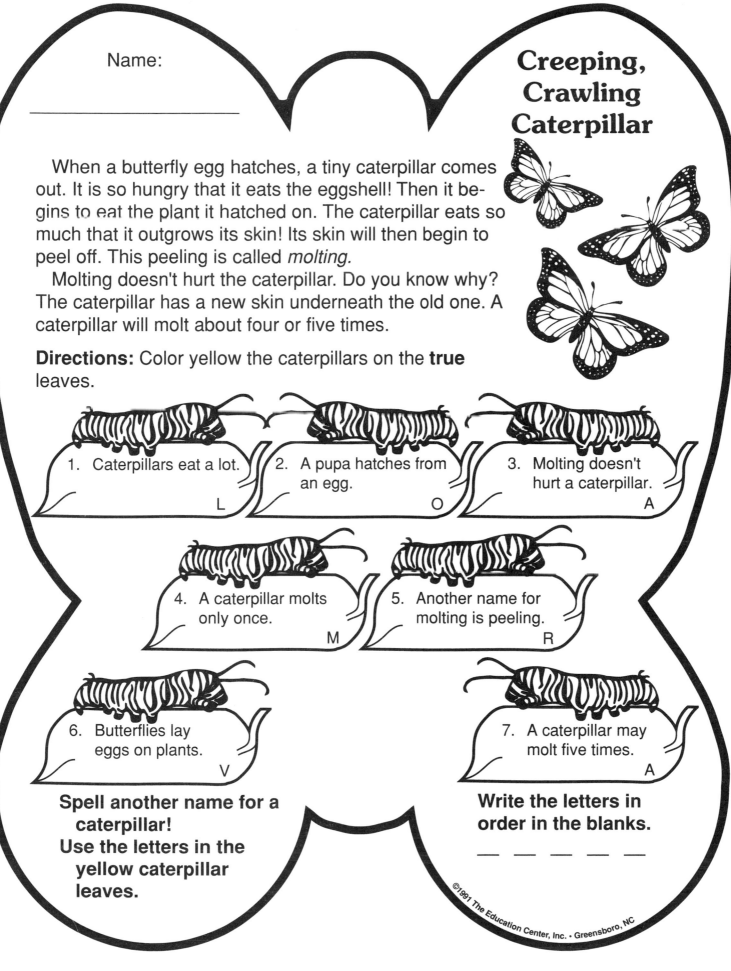

When a butterfly egg hatches, a tiny caterpillar comes out. It is so hungry that it eats the eggshell! Then it begins to eat the plant it hatched on. The caterpillar eats so much that it outgrows its skin! Its skin will then begin to peel off. This peeling is called *molting.*

Molting doesn't hurt the caterpillar. Do you know why? The caterpillar has a new skin underneath the old one. A caterpillar will molt about four or five times.

Directions: Color yellow the caterpillars on the **true** leaves.

1. Caterpillars eat a lot.
   L

2. A pupa hatches from an egg.
   O

3. Molting doesn't hurt a caterpillar.
   A

4. A caterpillar molts only once.
   M

5. Another name for molting is peeling.
   R

6. Butterflies lay eggs on plants.
   V

7. A caterpillar may molt five times.
   A

Spell another name for a caterpillar!
Use the letters in the yellow caterpillar leaves.

Write the letters in order in the blanks.

— — — — —

©1991 The Education Center, Inc. • Greensboro, NC

Note To Teacher: Explain to students that the butterfly (and its caterpillar) shown on this page is the monarch butterfly.

56

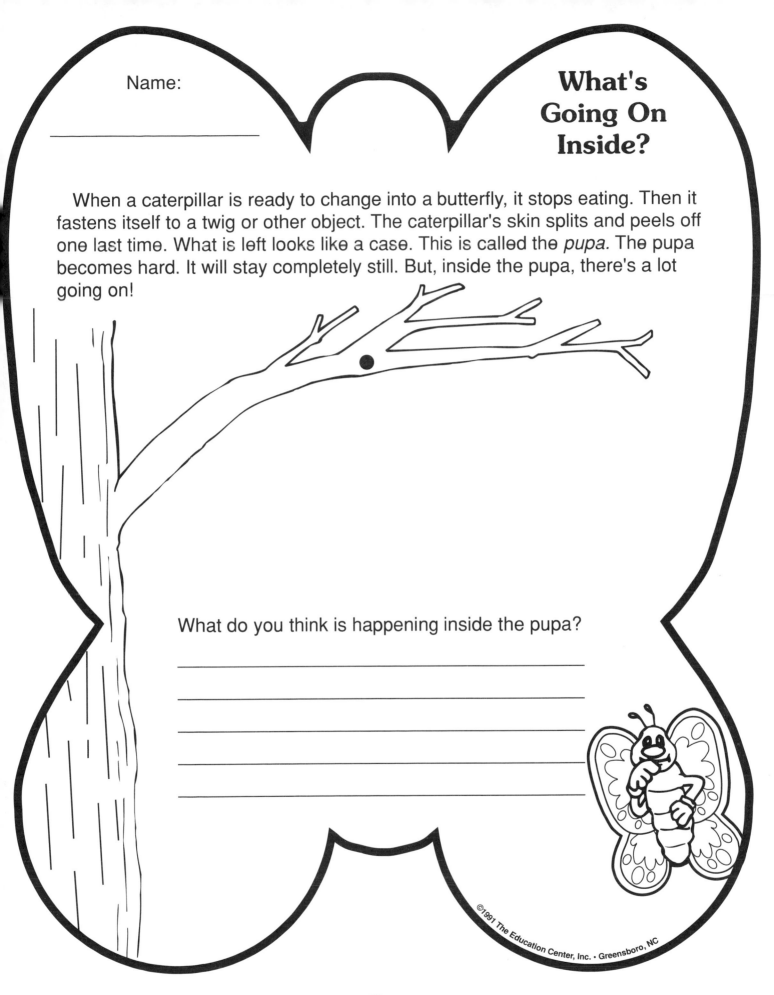

Name:

_____

What's Going On Inside?

When a caterpillar is ready to change into a butterfly, it stops eating. Then it fastens itself to a twig or other object. The caterpillar's skin splits and peels off one last time. What is left looks like a case. This is called the *pupa*. The pupa becomes hard. It will stay completely still. But, inside the pupa, there's a lot going on!

What do you think is happening inside the pupa?

_____

_____

_____

_____

_____

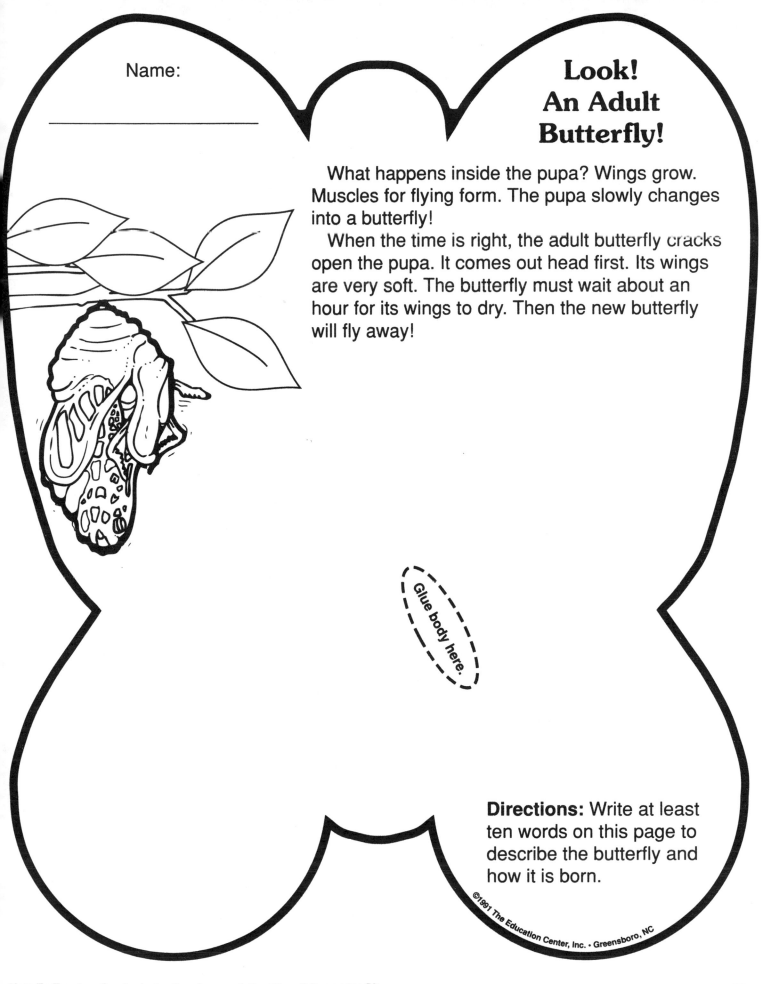

Name:

_____

Look!
An Adult
Butterfly!

What happens inside the pupa? Wings grow. Muscles for flying form. The pupa slowly changes into a butterfly!

When the time is right, the adult butterfly cracks open the pupa. It comes out head first. Its wings are very soft. The butterfly must wait about an hour for its wings to dry. Then the new butterfly will fly away!

Glue body here.

Directions: Write at least ten words on this page to describe the butterfly and how it is born.

Note To Teacher: See the instructions for completing this activity on page 59.

58

**Monarch
Pupa Pattern**

To complete page 57:
1. Have the student color the tree on page 57 with a brown crayon.
2. Duplicate the pupa pattern on white construction paper for each child.
3. Have each student color the pattern lightly with a brown crayon before cutting it out.
4. Have the student glue the pupa to page 57 at the •.
5. If desired, let the student cut leaves from green construction paper to glue on the twig.

Monarch Butterfly Pattern

To complete page 58:
1. Duplicate the butterfly pattern on white paper for each child.
2. Instruct students to color their butterflies according to this code:
   Orange = 1
   Brown = 2
3. After coloring, have students cut out their butterflies.
4. Have each child fold the wings of his butterfly on the dotted lines so that they are folded up slightly.
5. Glue the body and antennae of the butterfly *only* to page 58 where indicated.

Patterns for page 62

Name:

_____

Polyphemus Moth

Monarch Butterfly

Butterflies and moths are both insects. They look alike. They both have wings. They also both have a pair of antennae.

Butterflies are different from moths too. Most butterfly bodies are thin and smooth. Most moth bodies are fat and furry. The antennae of butterflies have knobs at the ends. Moth antennae are feathery.

Moths and butterflies are different in another way. Most butterflies fly during the day. Most moths fly at night.

Directions: Draw and color a new kind of moth or butterfly in the box. Try to use all the information you have learned.

Write a name for your moth or butterfly on this line:

_____

Name:

_____

Fooling The Enemy!

Butterflies protect themselves in many ways. Some are the same color as the plants they live near. This is called **camouflage**. For example, a brimstone butterfly's wings look like leaves.

Some butterflies and caterpillars look like other creatures. This is called **mimicry**. The owl butterfly has a large spot behind each back wing. To a bird or lizard, the spots look like the eyes of an owl. The tiger swallowtail caterpillar can arch its back so that it looks like a snake!

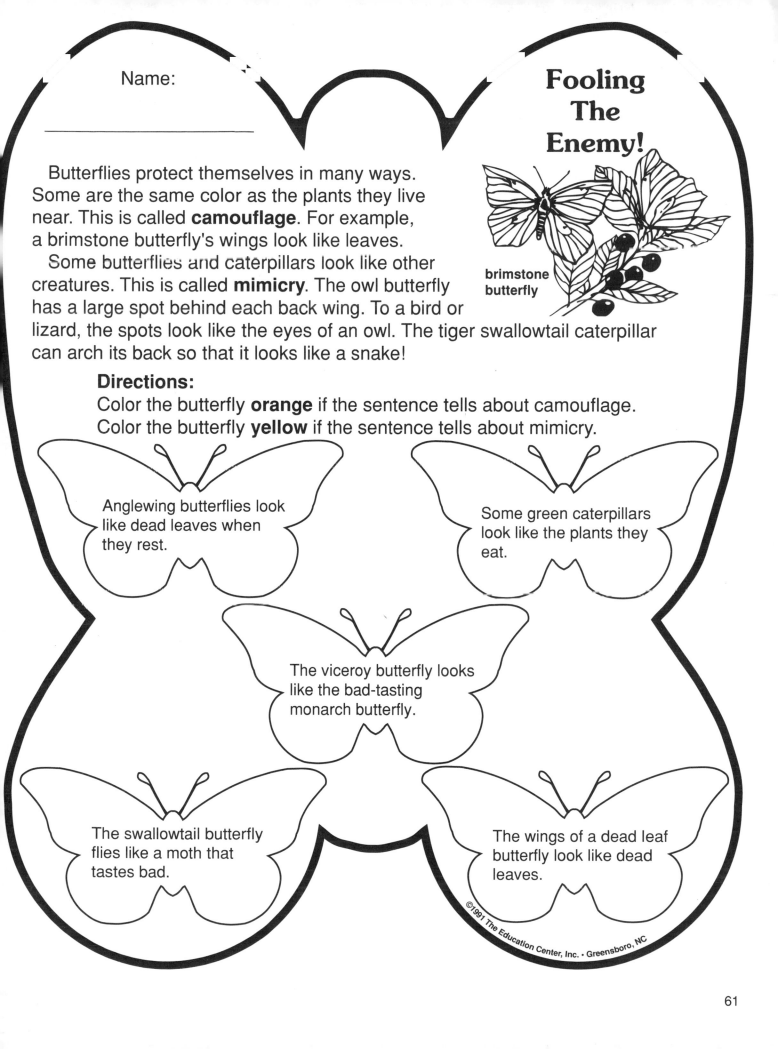

brimstone butterfly

Directions:
Color the butterfly **orange** if the sentence tells about camouflage.
Color the butterfly **yellow** if the sentence tells about mimicry.

Anglewing butterflies look like dead leaves when they rest.

Some green caterpillars look like the plants they eat.

The viceroy butterfly looks like the bad-tasting monarch butterfly.

The swallowtail butterfly flies like a moth that tastes bad.

The wings of a dead leaf butterfly look like dead leaves.

Name:

_____

Heading South

Some butterflies fly south each winter, just like birds do. They fly south so they can be in a warmer place. Monarch butterflies fly to places like Florida, California, and Mexico. They stay in these places until spring. Then they fly north to go back home.

Color the map according to the key.
Green = Florida
Orange = California
Yellow = Mexico

©1991 The Education Center, Inc. • Greensboro, NC

Note To Teacher: To finish this page, have students color, cut out, and paste the small monarch butterfly patterns on page 59 around the map.